PERCY JACKSON & THE OLYMPIANS

BOOK ONE

THE LIGHTNING THIEF

The Graphic Novel

by
RICK RIORDAN

Adapted by
Robert Venditti

Art by
Attila Futaki

Color by
José Villarrubia

Layouts by
Orpheus Collar

Lettering by
Chris Dickey

Disney·HYPERION
Los Angeles   New York

QUIET DOWN, CLASS.

NOW, WHO CAN TELL ME WHAT THE ENGRAVING ON THIS ANCIENT GREEK GRAVE MARKER REPRESENTS?

MR. JACKSON, PERHAPS?

OH, UM...

THAT'S... UH...KRONOS EATING HIS KIDS, RIGHT?

KRONOS WAS KING OF THE GODS, I MEAN...ER...THE TITANS, AND HE DIDN'T TRUST HIS KIDS-- THEY WERE THE GODS-- SO HE ATE THEM.

BUT HIS WIFE GAVE HIM A ROCK TO EAT INSTEAD OF ZEUS. AND WHEN ZEUS GREW UP, HE TRICKED DAD INTO...UM...BARFING UP THE OTHER KIDS. THEN THERE WAS A BIG GODS-VERSUS-TITANS WAR, AND THE GODS WON.

VERY NEARLY ADEQUATE, MR. JACKSON, SLANG FOR REGURGITATION NOTWITHSTANDING.

SO WHY DOES THIS STORY MATTER IN OUR LIVES? BEYOND EARNING A PASSING GRADE ON TOMORROW'S YEAR-END EXAMINATION.

BECAUSE...WELL, BECAUSE...

...I DON'T KNOW, MR. BRUNNER.

BUSTED!

I SEE. PERHAPS A LITTLE NOURISHMENT TO GET THE BRAIN WORKING AGAIN, HMM?

WE'LL CONTINUE OUR SEMESTER REVIEW AFTER LUNCH.

MR. JACKSON, I'LL HAVE A WORD WITH YOU ALONE, PLEASE.

NEW YORK CITY. THE METROPOLITAN MUSEUM OF ART.

ONE DAY UNTIL PERCY JACKSON EITHER PASSES THE SIXTH GRADE, OR GETS KICKED OUT OF HIS SIXTH SCHOOL IN AS MANY YEARS.

DETENTION AGAIN?

NAH. HE JUST WANTED TO REMIND ME THAT HIS CLASS ISN'T POINTLESS.

"WHAT YOU LEARN FROM ME IS *VITALLY* IMPORTANT, MR. JACKSON."

I LIKE BRUNNER AND ALL--

--BUT I WISH HE'D LAY OFF ME SOMETIMES. IT'S NOT LIKE I'M A *GENIUS*.

BUMMER. YOU GONNA EAT YOUR APPLE?

NICE GOING IN THERE, *DYSLEXIAC*.

IT'S DYSLE*XIC*. AND I'D RATHER BE AT BOARDING SCHOOL FOR TROUBLE WITH READING THAN BECAUSE I'M A CHRONIC *SHOPLIFTER*, KLEPTO-GIRL.

I STEAL THINGS BECAUSE I *LIKE* TO. DO YOU LIKE HAVING *MUSH* FOR BRAINS?

UH, GUYS? LET'S JUST EVERYBODY CALM DOWN.

FACE IT, REJECT. YOU'LL *ALWAYS* BE A LOSER.

SPLOOSH!

YOU'VE BEEN GIVING US PROBLEMS, YOUNG MAN. DID YOU *REALLY* THINK YOU WOULD GET AWAY WITH IT?

GET AWAY WITH WHAT? I SWEAR, I DON'T KNOW HOW NANCY GOT INTO THE FOUNTAIN...

WE ARE NOT *FOOLS*, PERCY JACKSON. *NO ONE* HIDES FROM US FOREVER.

CONFESS, AND YOU WILL SUFFER LESS PAIN.

MRS. DODDS? WHAT--

AH!

YOUR TIME IS UP!

EN GARDE, MR. JACKSON!

THE PEN--

--IS MIGHTIER--

--THAN THE SWORD!

SCREEE--

--EEEEE!

FOOMP

AH, *THERE'S* MY PEN.

PLEASE COME PREPARED WITH YOUR *OWN* WRITING INSTRUMENT IN THE FUTURE, MR. JACKSON.

SIR? WHAT HAPPENED TO... MRS. DODDS?

WHO?

MRS. DODDS. THE OTHER CHAPERONE... THE PRE-ALGEBRA TEACHER.

PERCY, THERE IS NO MRS. DODDS AT YANCY ACADEMY, AND AS FAR AS I CAN RECOLLECT, THERE NEVER HAS BEEN.

ARE YOU FEELING ALL RIGHT?

YANCY ACADEMY
EST. 1896

GREEK MYTHS

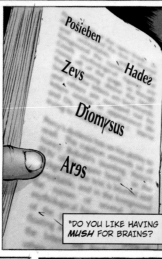

Pośieben

Zevs   Hades

Diomysus

Ares

"DO YOU LIKE HAVING *MUSH* FOR BRAINS?

"FACE IT, REJECT.

GREEK MYTHS

"YOU'LL *ALWAYS* BE A LOSER."

I'M **REALLY** WORRIED ABOUT PERCY.

HE SHOULDN'T BE ALONE OVER THE SUMMER BREAK. I MEAN, A **FURY** IN THE SCHOOL. NOW THAT WE KNOW FOR SURE, AND **THEY** KNOW, TOO...

WE WOULD ONLY MAKE MATTERS WORSE BY RUSHING HIM. HE NEEDS TIME TO MATURE.

BUT HE MIGHT NOT **HAVE** TIME. THE SUMMER SOLSTICE DEADLINE--

WILL HAVE TO BE RESOLVED WITHOUT HIM. LET HIM ENJOY HIS IGNORANCE WHILE HE STILL CAN.

I...I CAN'T FAIL AGAIN. YOU KNOW WHAT THAT WOULD MEAN FOR MY FUTURE.

YOU HAVEN'T FAILED, GROVER. I SHOULD HAVE SEEN HER FOR WHAT SHE WAS. NOW LET'S JUST WORRY ABOUT KEEPING THE BOY **ALIVE** UNTIL--

I THOUGHT I HEARD SOMEONE IN THE HALL. BLAST THESE NERVES--I HAVEN'T BEEN ON AN EVEN KEEL SINCE THE WINTER SOLSTICE.

YOU MAY RETURN TO YOUR DORMITORY. AND DON'T ASSUME THIS TURN OF EVENTS GIVES YOU A REPRIEVE FROM THE FINAL EXAMINATION.

UGH. NOT **ANOTHER** TEST.

EXAM DAY. A FEW SECONDS UNTIL--

TIME, CLASS. PENCILS DOWN, AND BRING YOUR TESTS FORWARD PLEASE.

IT'S PROBABLY NOT GOOD, MR. BRUNNER, BUT IT'S MY BEST.

TRY NOT TO BE DISCOURAGED, PERCY. YANCY ISN'T THE RIGHT PLACE FOR SOMEONE WITH YOUR... SPECIFIC LEARNING NEEDS.

IT WAS ONLY A MATTER OF TIME UNTIL EVERYONE RECOGNIZED THAT.

SIR?

OH, *CONFOUND* IT ALL. WHAT I MEAN TO SAY IS... YOU'RE NOT NORMAL, PERCY. HOWEVER, THAT'S NOTHING TO BE ASHAMED--

THANKS FOR THE REMINDER. I'D *ALMOST* FORGOT.

BUS 108 FROM ITHACA, NOW ARRIVING.

YOU JUST GOING TO LEAVE WITHOUT SAYING GOOD-BYE TO YOUR BEST FRIEND?

SORRY...I'VE MOVED SCHOOLS SO MUCH, I'M KINDA USED TO LEAVING UNANNOUNCED.

YOU LOOKING FOR MORE *"FURIES"*?

WHA-- WHAT DO YOU MEAN?

NICE TRY. I HEARD YOU AND BRUNNER TALKING IN HIS OFFICE LAST NIGHT.

LOOK...I WAS JUST WORRIED ABOUT YOU, IS ALL. HALLUCINATING ABOUT *DEMON MATH TEACHERS...*

I TOLD HIM THAT MAYBE YOU WERE STRESSED OR SOMETHING, BECAUSE...LIKE...THERE WAS NO MRS. DODDS, AND--

PERCY... TELL ME THOSE OLD LADIES AREN'T STARING AT YOU.

LOOKS LIKE IT.
THOSE SOCKS ARE A
LITTLE *BIG* FOR ME,
THOUGH.

NOT FUNNY.
YOU DO *NOT* WANT
TO WEAR THOSE
SOCKS.

SNIP!

SHE
SNIPPED THE STRING!
DID YOU SEE THAT?!
SHE SNIPPED THE STRING!

WHAT'S THE BIG DEAL?
YOU DON'T THINK THEY'LL
COME OVER HERE,
DO YOU?

SIXTH GRADE.
ALWAYS *SIXTH
GRADE*...

WAIT HERE,
OKAY? I'M GOING TO
BUY A TICKET AND RIDE
INTO THE CITY WITH YOU.
JUST *WAIT HERE.*

MANHATTAN'S UPPER EAST SIDE.

HOME SWEET HOME.

SWEETHEART!

I LEFT WORK JUST AS SOON AS THEY'D LET ME. I COULDN'T WAIT TO SEE YOU.

HEY, MOM.

LOOK HOW YOU'VE GROWN SINCE CHRISTMAS! OH, I MISS OUT ON SO MUCH.

SORRY ABOUT YOUR ROOM.... YOUR STEPFATHER WANTED A PLACE WHERE HE COULD READ HIS CAR MAGAZINES.

HE NEEDS A WHOLE ROOM? COULDN'T HE DO THAT IN A *CHAIR*?

SALLY! BEAN DIP!

NEVER MIND THAT. I'VE GOT A SURPRISE FOR YOU--

--WE'RE GOING TO THE BEACH! I RENTED OUR USUAL PLACE FOR *THREE WHOLE NIGHTS*.

REALLY?! WHEN DO WE LEAVE?

THE MINUTE I GET CHANGED.

BEAN DIP! AREN'T YOU LISTENING?

YES, DEAR. I'LL MAKE IT WHILE PERCY PACKS FOR OUR TRIP.

RIGHT. YOUR *TRIP*. I WANT YOUR KID'S WORD THAT MY *CAR* WILL COME BACK IN THE SAME CONDITION IT LEFT. NOT ONE SCRATCH.

I'M *TWELVE*. IT'S NOT LIKE I'LL BE DRIVING THE THING.

NOT.

ONE.

SCRATCH.

SURE THING, GABE. IT'S THE *LEAST* I CAN DO.

THAT'S MORE LIKE IT. A MAN COMMANDS *RESPECT* IN HIS OWN HOME.

THE FELLAS WILL BE HERE FOR THE POKER GAME IN *FIVE*, SALLY, AND THAT DIP *BETTER* BE ON THE TABLE.

YES, DEAR.

CHIN UP, SWEETHEART. IN A FEW HOURS WE'LL BE OCEANSIDE...

"...AND ALL OUR HEADACHES WILL BE GONE."

NOW *THIS* IS THE LIFE.

·YOU'RE KIDDING, RIGHT? WE'VE GOT NO POWER AND THERE'S, LIKE, A *HURRICANE* GOING ON OUTSIDE.

I'LL TAKE IT. THIS PLACE HAS SUCH *GOOD* MEMORIES FOR ME. IT'S WHERE I MET YOUR FATHER, YOU KNOW. WE SPENT THE SUMMER TOGETHER.

HE KNEW I WAS EXPECTING A BABY. BUT HE HAD TO SET SAIL, AND WE NEVER SAW EACH OTHER AGAIN. HE WAS... LOST AT SEA.

THERE'S A LOT OF HIM IN YOU. YOUR EYES, YOUR HAIR...

MY D+ REPORT CARD? I'M PRETTY SURE YANCY WON'T BE INVITING ME BACK NEXT YEAR, MOM.

GROVER?

SEARCHING ALL NIGHT -*HUFF*-

WHAT WERE YOU -*HUFF*- THINKING?

LOOK, I'M SORRY I DITCHED YOU AT THE BUS DEPOT, BUT--

IT'S *RIGHT BEHIND* ME, MRS. JACKSON-- WE HAVE TO LEAVE!

PERCY, DID SOMETHING HAPPEN AT SCHOOL? WHAT HAVEN'T YOU TOLD ME?

NOTHING. I...

GROVER, WHAT'S WITH YOUR *LEGS*?

PERCY! TELL ME *NOW!*

THERE WAS THIS TEACHER, AND SHE WAS LIKE A BAT-LADY OR SOMETHING. BUT EVERYONE SAID SHE NEVER EXISTED, SO--

GET TO THE CAR, BOTH OF YOU! GO!

MOM? SOME...*THING* IS COMING.

MWOOROOOR

TAKE GROVER AND HEAD TOWARD THAT TALL PINE. THAT'S THE PROPERTY LINE. ON THE OTHER SIDE OF THE HILL IS A FARMHOUSE. *DON'T STOP* UNTIL YOU GET THERE.

BUT WHAT ABOUT YOU?! I'M NOT LEAVING YOU.

I'LL BE FINE. IT'S NOT *ME* THEY WANT.

JUST *GO!*

...FOOD...

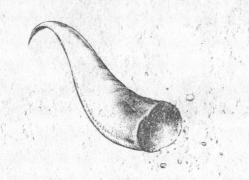

WHERE ARE WE? DID I CATCH THE FLU OR SOMETHING?

I'M ALL ACHY, AND MAN DID I HAVE SOME *FUNKY* DREAMS.

YOU'VE BEEN OUT FOR TWO DAYS. HOW MUCH DO YOU REMEMBER?

~:GROAN:~

I DREAMED ABOUT SOME BLOND GIRL WHO KEPT CALLING ME "THE ONE." AND IN THIS OTHER DREAM, YOU WERE HALF GOAT, AND WE FOUGHT A COW.

THE SCARIEST PART OF *THAT ONE* WAS WHAT HAPPENED TO MY MOM.

YOU SAVED MY LIFE, PERCY. I...THOUGHT YOU MIGHT WANT THIS. IT WAS THE LEAST I COULD DO.

OH, NO. MY MOM...IS SHE REALLY...?

IT'S ALL MY FAULT. I'M THE WORST SATYR IN THE WORLD. WE TOLD YOUR MOM I'D PROTECT YOU, BUT I MADE A MESS OF EVERYTHING. *AGAIN*.

DOES THIS HAVE ANYTHING TO DO WITH THE OLD LADIES AT THE BUS STATION?

THOSE WEREN'T OLD LADIES. THEY WERE THE THREE FATES.

THEY ONLY CUT THE STRING WHEN SOMEONE IS ABOUT TO...YOU KNOW.

MOM...

DRINK THIS. IT'LL HELP YOU HEAL.

THEN I THINK IT'S TIME YOU TALKED TO CHIRON AND MR. D.

THIS IS MR. D., OUR CAMP DIRECTOR.

WELCOME TO CAMP HALF-BLOOD, BLAH, BLAH, BLAH. NOW DON'T EXPECT ME TO BE *GLAD* TO SEE YOU.

AND YOU, UM, ALREADY KNOW OUR ACTIVITIES DIRECTOR.

"MR. BRUNNER" WAS A PSEUDONYM. YOU MAY CALL ME CHIRON NOW.

AND I MUST SAY, PERCY, I'M PLEASED TO SEE YOU ALIVE. I DON'T OFTEN VISIT A POTENTIAL CAMPER AT A SCHOOL FOR *MORTALS*.

I'D HATE TO THINK I'D WASTED MY TIME.

LET'S NOT *RUSH TO JUDGMENT*, CHIRON. YOU MAY YET DISCOVER THAT YOU'VE WASTED YOUR TIME ON THIS BOY.

OH, I DON'T KNOW. GROVER SENSED SOMETHING SPECIAL IN HIM.

A *RINGING ENDORSEMENT*, TO BE SURE.

I'LL... UH... BE GOING THEN.

GOOD RIDDANCE.

EXCUSE MR. D. FOR BEING GRUFF, PERCY. HE'S BEEN GROUNDED SINCE HE TOOK A FANCY TO A WOOD NYMPH HIS FATHER DECLARED OFF-LIMITS.

HOW FATHER *LOVES* TO PUNISH ME. SENDING ME HERE TO RUN A SUMMER CAMP FOR *BRATS* LIKE YOU.

I *TRIED* TO BEHAVE, BUT SHE WAS VERY PRETTY, AND YOU KNOW HOW THINGS PROGRESS WHEN THE *WINE* IS FLOWING...

REMEMBER YOUR RESTRICTIONS, MR. D.

-:HUMPF:- *OLD HABITS,* AND ALL OF THAT. APOLOGIES TO MY FATHER.

WHO EXACTLY *IS* YOUR FATHER?

DI IMMORTALES, CHIRON. I THOUGHT YOU TAUGHT THIS BOY THE BASICS. MY FATHER IS *ZEUS*, OF COURSE.

ZEUS'S SON... MR. D...YOU'RE SAYING THAT YOU'RE *DIONYSUS*, THE GOD OF WINE?

THE GOD OF *COLA*, IT WOULD SEEM. AT LEAST UNTIL *DEAR OLD DAD* SAYS OTHERWISE.

I DON'T UNDERSTAND. WHAT IS THIS PLACE? WHY WOULD YOU GO TO YANCY JUST TO TEACH ME, MR. BRUN-- UM, CHIRON?

WHAT HAPPENED TO MY MOM?

THERE'S SO MUCH TO EXPLAIN. PERHAPS A GUIDED TOUR IS IN ORDER.

COME ALONG, PERCY--

YOU MAY NOT REALIZE IT, PERCY, BUT GREAT POWERS ARE AT WORK IN YOUR LIFE.

THE MYTHS YOU REFER TO AS THE "GREEK GODS" ARE VERY REAL, AND VERY MUCH ALIVE. THEY ALWAYS HAVE BEEN, AND ALWAYS WILL BE.

DO THOSE HORSES HAVE **WINGS**?

AS WILL OLYMPUS. NOT **MOUNT** OLYMPUS, MIND YOU, WHICH IS IN GREECE, BUT THE **PALACE** OF OLYMPUS. THE GATHERING PLACE OF THE GODS.

IS THERE **LAVA** COMING OUT OF THAT CLIMBING WALL?

"YOU SEE, THE GODS-- AND OLYMPUS--MOVE WITH THE HEART OF WESTERN CIVILIZATION."

"THEY BEGAN IN GREECE, THEN MOVED TO ROME. FOR THE PAST CENTURY THEY'VE BEEN HERE, IN AMERICA."

YOU MIGHT SAY THAT THE GODS ARE THE **SOURCE** OF THE WEST. OR AT LEAST BOUND SO TIGHTLY TO IT THAT THEY COULDN'T POSSIBLY FADE, NOT UNLESS ALL OF WESTERN CIVILIZATION WERE OBLITERATED.

ARE YOU REALLY...?

THE CHIRON FROM THE STORIES? TRAINER OF HERCULES AND ALL THAT?

YES, PERCY. I AM.

I GUESS THIS IS WHAT YOU MEANT WHEN YOU SAID WHAT I LEARNED IN YOUR CLASS WAS "VITALLY IMPORTANT."

SO...IF THE GODS AND OLYMPUS ARE REAL, THEN DOES THAT MEAN THE *UNDERWORLD* IS REAL, TOO? THAT... PEOPLE WHO DIE AREN'T REALLY...

WHAT DO YOU MEAN, "UNTIL WE--"?

AH, ANNABETH, RIGHT ON SCHEDULE. I KNOW YOU'RE BUSY PREPARING FOR FRIDAY'S GAME, BUT WOULD YOU MIND TAKING OUR NEWEST ARRIVAL TO CABIN ELEVEN? I HAVE ANOTHER ENGAGEMENT.

YES, CHILD. THERE IS A PLACE WHERE SPIRITS GO AFTER DEATH, BUT UNTIL WE KNOW MORE, I WOULD URGE YOU TO PUT THAT THOUGHT OUT OF YOUR MIND.

YOU'RE MY DREAM GIRL.

EXCUSE ME?

I'LL SEE YOU AT THE EVENING MEAL, PERCY.

WHAT I MEAN IS...ER... I DREAMED ABOUT YOU.

THAT WASN'T A *DREAM*. I HELPED CHIRON AND THE OTHERS NURSE YOU BACK TO HEALTH.

FOLLOW ME.

LOOK, I'M SORRY. I DON'T EVEN KNOW WHAT I'M DOING HERE. ALL I KNOW IS, I KILL SOME BULL-GUY--

MONSTERS *DON'T DIE.*

YOU CAN *DISPEL* THEM FOR A WHILE--MAYBE EVEN A WHOLE LIFETIME IF YOU CATCH A BREAK--BUT *EVENTUALLY* THEY RE-FORM.

JEEZ, TAKE IT EASY. YOU'RE ACTING LIKE I DID SOMETHING WRONG.

EVERY KID IN CAMP *WISHES* THEY'D HAD YOUR CHANCE TO FIGHT. IT'S WHAT WE TRAIN FOR. YOU DON'T KNOW HOW LUCKY YOU ARE.

LUCKY, RIGHT. AS IF YOU KNOW *ANYTHING* ABOUT WHAT IT'S LIKE TO BE ME.

NO?

YOU MOVE SCHOOLS A LOT. PROBABLY GET *KICKED OUT* OF MOST OF THEM. PLUS, YOU'VE BEEN DIAGNOSED WITH *DYSLEXIA*, AND MAYBE *ADHD*, TOO. TAKEN TOGETHER, THEY'RE ALMOST A SURE SIGN.

WHO TOLD YOU--?

READING ENGLISH GIVES YOU FITS BECAUSE YOUR BRAIN IS HARDWIRED FOR *ANCIENT GREEK.*

THE HYPERACTIVITY? THAT'S YOUR BATTLEFIELD INSTINCTS KICKING IN. NO *REGULAR* HUMAN COULD CHARGE A MONSTER, *ESPECIALLY* MR. MOO, AND SURVIVE.

FACE IT. YOU'RE ONE OF US. YOU'RE A *HALF-BLOOD.*

CHECK OUT THE *NEWBIE!*

CLARISSE, WHY DON'T YOU GO POLISH YOUR SPEAR OR SOMETHING?

SURE THING, MISS PRINCESS. THEN I'LL *RUN YOU THROUGH* WITH IT.

WHO'S THE LITTLE RUNT?

PERCY, MEET CLARISSE, DAUGHTER OF *ARES*.

LIKE... THE WAR GOD?

I'M ALSO HEAD OF THE *UNOFFICIAL* WELCOMING COMMITTEE.

CLARISSE! DON'T!

HEY!

LET ME SHOW YOU HOW *WE* SAY "WELCOME!"

LET GO!

HAVE A *DRINK*, NEWBIE. IT'S ON ME.

RUMMMMBLE

CABIN ELEVEN. I'VE GOT TRAINING TO GET TO. WHEN YOU HEAR THE CONCH, FALL IN WITH YOUR CABIN AND HEAD TO THE PAVILION FOR DINNER.

YOU MUST BE PERCY. I'M LUKE, YOUR HEAD COUNSELOR FOR THE TIME BEING.

EVERYBODY, *LISTEN UP!* THIS IS PERCY JACKSON, OUR NEW CABINMATE.

REGULAR OR *UNDETERMINED?*

UNDETERMINED.

AW, MAN...

SUPER.

NOT *ANOTHER* ONE!

DON'T MIND THEM. AS YOU CAN SEE, WE'RE A LITTLE CROWDED IN HERE.

I CAN SLEEP IN THE CABIN WITH THE LIGHTNING BOLT OVER THE DOOR. IT LOOKED EMPTY AND A LITTLE... UM...NEWER.

UNFORTUNATELY, WE DON'T GET TO PICK OUR CABINS. IT DEPENDS ON WHO YOUR PARENTS ARE. OR *PARENT*.

THIS IS ONE OF *THOSE* CAMPS, HUH?

WELL, DON'T COUNT ON GETTING A DONATION CHECK FROM MY MOM. SHE'S...GONE.

I'M SORRY ABOUT YOUR MOM, PERCY, BUT THAT'S NOT WHAT I MEANT. I'M TALKING ABOUT YOUR *OTHER* PARENT.

MY DAD? DON'T HOLD YOUR BREATH WAITING FOR HIM TO *PAY UP*, EITHER. HE DIED BEFORE I WAS BORN.

AND DON'T GET ME STARTED ON MY *STEP*DAD...

YOUR DAD ISN'T DEAD. HE *CAN'T* BE.

HOW WOULD YOU KNOW? YOU SAYING YOU'VE MET HIM?

I DON'T HAVE TO.

I KNOW YOU'RE HERE, WHICH CAN MEAN JUST ONE THING: YOU'RE ONLY *HALF* HUMAN.

WHAT? THEN WHAT'S THE OTHER HALF?

CONSIDERING WHAT YOU'VE SEEN TODAY, I THINK YOU KNOW.

WHO IS HE, THEN?

UNDETERMINED. NOBODY KNOWS.

MAYBE HE'LL SEND A SIGN AND CLAIM YOU, THOUGH. THAT HAPPENS SOMETIMES.

MEANING THAT SOMETIMES IT DOESN'T?

MORE THAN SOMETIMES...

THERE ARE KIDS IN HERE THAT HAVE BEEN UNDETERMINED FOR *YEARS.*

ARE *YOU* UNDETERMINED?

NAW. MY OLD MAN IS HERMES. I EVEN GOT TO MEET HIM.

ONCE.

ANYWAY, YOU CAN STAY WITH US AS LONG AS YOU NEED TO. HERMES ISN'T PICKY ABOUT WHO HE SPONSORS--ANYBODY WHO USES THE ROADS IS FAIR GAME. MESSENGERS, TRAVELERS, MERCHANTS...

EVEN *THIEVES*. SO WATCH YOUR STUFF AROUND THIS LOT. SPEAKING OF WHICH...

I HEARD YOU PACKED LIGHT, SO I NICKED SOME TOILETRIES FROM THE CAMP SUPPLY SHOP TO GET YOU STARTED.

THANKS.

YOU KNOW, BESIDES CHIRON AND GROVER, YOU'RE THE ONLY PERSON I'VE MET THAT HASN'T TREATED ME LIKE A *DISEASE*.

LISTEN, PERCY. I KNOW IT'S A LOT TO TAKE IN, BUT THE FIRST DAY IS ALWAYS THE WORST. AFTER ALL, EVERYONE HERE IS EXTENDED FAMILY, RIGHT? WHEN PUSH COMES TO SHOVE, WE TAKE CARE OF EACH OTHER.

THERE *WILL* BE PUSHING AND SHOVING, THOUGH. YOU'RE THE NEW KID, SO YOU'LL HAVE TO EARN YOUR OWN REP, STARTING WITH FRIDAY'S GAME OF CAPTURE THE FLAG.

DO I HAVE TO PLAY? I'VE BEEN *UNCONSCIOUS* THE PAST COUPLE OF DAYS.

EVERYBODY PLAYS. CAMP RULES. BUT DON'T SWEAT IT, OKAY? WE'LL START TRAINING FIRST THING TOMORROW.

WHO KNOWS? WE FIND WHAT YOU'RE GOOD AT, AND MAYBE WE'LL GET A CLUE AS TO WHO *SIRED* YOU.

FRIDAY NIGHT.

ATTENTION, CAMPERS. LET'S GET THIS OVER WITH.

FOR TONIGHT'S GAME OF CAPTURE THE FLAG, THE BLUE TEAM, LED BY ANNABETH FROM CABIN SIX, HAS ALLIED WITH CABINS SEVEN AND ELEVEN. THE RED TEAM, LED BY CLARISSE FROM CABIN FIVE, IS JOINED BY CABINS FOUR, NINE, TEN, AND TWELVE. CABIN FIVE, *ARES*, IS THE CURRENT CHAMPION. HUZZAH.

YOU ALL KNOW THE RULES: THE CREEK IS THE BOUNDARY LINE, AND THE ENTIRE FOREST IS FAIR GAME. MAGIC ITEMS ARE PERMITTED. KILLING AND MAIMING-- MUCH TO MY *REGRET*-- ARE NOT.

CHIRON WILL SERVE AS REFEREE AND BATTLEFIELD MEDIC, IN THE HAPPY EVENT THAT ONE OF YOU WHELPS IS INJURED. SHOULD ANYONE NEED *ME*, I'LL BE AT THE BIG HOUSE, PONDERING MY IGNOMINY.

LET THE GAME BEGIN. GOOD LUCK, BLAH, BLAH, BLAH...

SO, SHOULD I GO AFTER THE RED TEAM'S FLAG?

YEAH, RIGHT. AFTER THE WEEK OF "TRAINING" YOU'VE HAD?

YOU CAN TAKE BORDER PATROL BY THE CREEK, AS *FAR* FROM THE ACTION AS POSSIBLE. LEAVE THE REST TO ME.

GEE, GLAD YOU WANTED ME ON YOUR TEAM...

CREAM THE PUNK!

WHOA!

CHK!

INVISIBILITY HAT. PRETTY COOL, RIGHT? MY MOM GAVE IT TO ME FOR--

YOU *KNEW* CLARISSE WAS GUNNING FOR ME, SO YOU STUCK ME HERE *ALONE* TO GET SKEWERED AND SENT LUKE AFTER THE FLAG. YOU SET ME UP.

YEAH. MOM WOULD BE SO *PROUD*.

YOU ALMOST GOT ME *KILLED!*

WHAT KIND OF MOM WOULD BE PROUD OF A KID WHO DID THAT?

ATHENA, OF COURSE. GODDESS OF WISDOM AND BATTLE.

NATURALLY.

AW, DON'T GET SO BENT OUT OF SHAPE. I CAME TO HELP AS FAST AS I COULD. TURNS OUT YOU DIDN'T NEED IT, THOUGH.

WHEN DID YOU LEARN TO FIGHT LIKE THAT?

I *DIDN'T.* FALLING IN THE CREEK MUST'VE REALLY MADE ME MAD, BECAUSE ALL OF A SUDDEN I HAD, LIKE, A BERSERKER REFLEX.

THE CREEK, HUH...?

rUstle
rustle

HOW? THE BREASTPLATE WAS BREACHED. I *SAW* THE BEAST'S CLAWS FIND THEIR MARK...

THE WATER, CHIRON.

SO WHAT? A *MAGIC CREEK* IS HARDLY THE WEIRDEST THING I'VE SEEN AT THIS CAMP.

THE *CREEK* DOESN'T HAVE POWER, PERCY. *YOU* DO.

LOOK.

THE BLOODLINE IS *DETERMINED.*

POSEIDON-- EARTHSHAKER, STORMBRINGER, LORD OF HORSES.

HAIL PERSEUS JACKSON, SON OF THE SEA GOD.

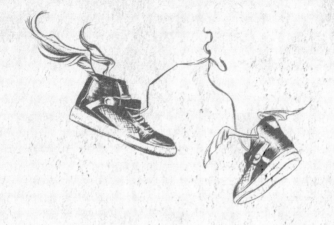

NO!

KNOCK KNOCK

GROVER! I COULD MAKE A JOKE ABOUT THE *LAST* TIME YOU KNOCKED ON MY DOOR, BUT, HECK, I'M JUST GLAD TO SEE YOU.

COME ON IN AND I'LL SHOW YOU MY NEW DIGS.

IT'S BIG, ALL RIGHT. AND *EMPTY*. I NEVER THOUGHT I'D SAY IT, BUT I ACTUALLY *MISS* THE HERMES CROWD.

LUKE STILL HANGS OUT WITH ME, BUT THE REST OF THE CAMPERS KEEP THEIR DISTANCE. THAT INCLUDES *CLARISSE*, THOUGH, SO IT ISN'T *ALL* BAD.

WHAT'S WRONG? DON'T TELL ME EVEN MY *BEST FRIEND* IS CUTTING ME LOOSE...

THERE'S A *REASON* EVERYONE IS KEEPING THEIR DISTANCE.

COME WITH ME TO THE BIG HOUSE. CHIRON CAN EXPLAIN EVERYTHING.

YOU NEVER SHOULD HAVE BEEN BORN.

"YOU SEE, THE WAR HAD BEEN THE RESULT OF A *SPAT* BETWEEN THE SONS OF ZEUS AND POSEIDON ON ONE SIDE, AND THE SONS OF HADES ON THE OTHER.

YOU *REALLY* NEED TO WORK ON YOUR DELIVERY.

AFTER WORLD WAR II, THE THREE SONS OF KRONOS--ZEUS, POSEIDON, AND HADES--MADE A PACT NEVER TO SIRE ANY MORE HALF-BLOODS.

THEIR OFFSPRING WERE AFFECTING THE COURSE OF HUMAN EVENTS TOO MUCH.

"SO THE BROTHERS SWORE AN OATH ON THE *RIVER STYX*, AND THE PACT WAS UPHELD...

"...UNTIL SEVENTEEN YEARS AGO. ZEUS FELL OFF THE WAGON, AS IT WERE, AND HAD A *DAUGHTER* WITH AN AMERICAN TV STARLET.

"THE CHILD'S NAME WAS THALIA, AND SHE WAS TWELVE WHEN HADES LEARNED OF HER. FURIOUS, HE LOOSED HIS WORST MONSTERS TO DESTROY HER.

"A *SATYR* WAS DISPATCHED TO BRING HER SAFELY TO CAMP. THEY--AND TWO OTHER HALF-BLOODS THEY MET ALONG THE WAY--*NEARLY* MADE IT.

"WOUNDED AND WEARY OF THE CHASE, THALIA MADE HER FINAL STAND JUST OUTSIDE THE VALLEY, SACRIFICING HERSELF SO THAT HER COMPANIONS COULD MAKE IT TO SAFETY."

AS SHE PERISHED, ZEUS TOOK PITY ON HER AND TRANSFORMED HER INTO A PINE TREE. HER SPIRIT PROTECTS THE CAMP'S BORDERS TO THIS DAY.

THAT WAS THE *LAST TIME* A CHILD OF THE BROTHERS WAS DETERMINED. UNTIL YOU.

THAT'S NOT FAIR!

IT WASN'T THE GIRL'S FAULT THAT HER DAD COULDN'T KEEP HIS WORD.

INDEED. BUT WHEN THE BROTHERS SET TO BICKERING, FAIRNESS RARELY ENTERS INTO THE EQUATION. A TRUTH YOU MAY WELL LEARN *FIRSTHAND*.

ZEUS AND POSEIDON ARE FIGHTING NOW, AREN'T THEY? OVER SOMETHING THAT WAS STOLEN...SOMETHING VALUABLE.

I HAD A DREAM...

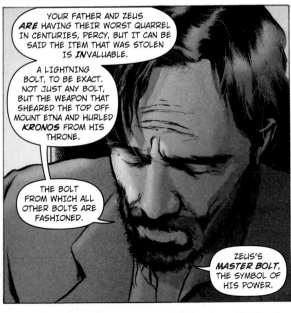

I KNEW IT!

HUSH, SATYR.

BUT IT'S HIS QUEST! IT *MUST* BE!

YOUR FATHER AND ZEUS *ARE* HAVING THEIR WORST QUARREL IN CENTURIES, PERCY, BUT IT CAN BE SAID THE ITEM THAT WAS STOLEN IS *IN*VALUABLE.

A LIGHTNING BOLT, TO BE EXACT. NOT JUST ANY BOLT, BUT THE WEAPON THAT SHEARED THE TOP OFF MOUNT ETNA AND HURLED *KRONOS* FROM HIS THRONE.

THE BOLT FROM WHICH ALL OTHER BOLTS ARE FASHIONED.

ZEUS'S *MASTER BOLT*, THE SYMBOL OF HIS POWER.

AND *YOU* ARE THE THIEF.

BUT--

AT LEAST, THAT IS WHAT ZEUS CLAIMS. AND PERHAPS NOT WITHOUT CAUSE.

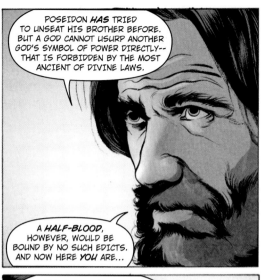

POSEIDON *HAS* TRIED TO UNSEAT HIS BROTHER BEFORE. BUT A GOD CANNOT USURP ANOTHER GOD'S SYMBOL OF POWER DIRECTLY-- THAT IS FORBIDDEN BY THE MOST ANCIENT OF DIVINE LAWS.

A *HALF-BLOOD*, HOWEVER, WOULD BE BOUND BY NO SUCH EDICTS. AND NOW HERE *YOU* ARE...

THIEVERY IS NOT POSEIDON'S STYLE, BUT HE IS TOO PROUD TO TRY CONVINCING ZEUS OF THAT.

THEY ARE DEADLOCKED: ZEUS DEMANDS HIS BOLT BE RETURNED, AND POSEIDON DEMANDS AN APOLOGY FOR BEING WRONGLY ACCUSED.

THEY'VE SET THE SUMMER SOLSTICE--TEN DAYS FROM NOW-- AS THE DEADLINE. IF THE MATTER IS NOT RESOLVED BY THEN, THERE WILL BE *WAR*.

OLYMPIANS WILL BE FORCED TO CHOOSE SIDES. THERE WILL BE CHAOS. DESTRUCTION. AND WESTERN CIVILIZATION WILL BE THE BATTLEGROUND.

AND YOU'RE TELLING ME ALL OF THIS BECAUSE...

IF POSEIDON DIDN'T STEAL THE BOLT-- AND I DON'T BELIEVE HE DID--THEN WHAT BETTER PEACE OFFERING THAN TO HAVE HIS *SON* RETRIEVE IT?

YOU WANT *ME* TO FIND THE STUPID THING?

WHERE SHOULD I LOOK FIRST? UNDER MY PILLOW?

I MAY HAVE AN INKLING. PART OF A PROPHECY I HAD YEARS AGO... SOME OF THE LINES MAKE SENSE TO ME NOW.

BUT BEFORE I SAY MORE, YOU MUST SEEK THE COUNSEL OF THE ORACLE. GO UPSTAIRS, TO THE ATTIC. WHEN YOU COME BACK DOWN, WE'LL RESUME.

"ASSUMING YOU'RE STILL **SANE**."

GAH!

CREAK

I AM THE SSSPIRIT OF DELPHI, SPEAKER OF THE PROPHECIES OF PHOEBUSSS APOLLO, SLAYER OF THE MIGHTY PYTHON.

APPROACH, SEEKER, AND ASSSK.

WH-WHAT IS MY DESTINY?

YOU SHALL GO WESSST, AND FACE THE GOD WHO HAS TURNED.

YOU SHALL FIND WHAT WAS STOLEN, AND SSSEE IT SAFELY RETURNED.

AND YOU SHALL FAIL TO SSSAVE WHAT MATTERS MOSSST IN THE END.

YOU SHALL BE BETRAYED BY ONE WHO CALLSSS YOU FRIEND.

WAIT! DON'T GO!

WHAT FRIEND?

WHAT WILL I FAIL TO SAVE?

IT...*SHE* SAID I WOULD GO WEST AND FACE THE GOD WHO HAS TURNED. I WOULD RETRIEVE WHAT WAS STOLEN AND SEE IT SAFELY RETURNED.

I TOLD YOU HE WAS THE ONE!

IT IS CRUCIAL THAT YOU TELL ME EVERYTHING. WAS THERE NOTHING *MORE*?

VERY WELL. BUT KNOW THIS: THE ORACLE'S WORDS OFTEN HAVE *DOUBLE MEANINGS*. THE TRUTH IS NOT ALWAYS CLEAR UNTIL EVENTS COME TO PASS.

UH...NOPE.

SO...WHO'S THIS GOD IN THE WEST?

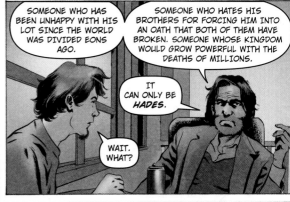

SOMEONE WHO HAS BEEN UNHAPPY WITH HIS LOT SINCE THE WORLD WAS DIVIDED EONS AGO.

SOMEONE WHO HATES HIS BROTHERS FOR FORCING HIM INTO AN OATH THAT BOTH OF THEM HAVE BROKEN. SOMEONE WHOSE KINGDOM WOULD GROW POWERFUL WITH THE DEATHS OF MILLIONS.

IT CAN ONLY BE *HADES*.

WAIT. WHAT?

REMEMBER THAT MRS. DODDS WAS A FURY. THEY OBEY ONLY THE LORD OF THE DEAD.

THERE MUST BE A SPY IN CAMP AS WELL, SOMEONE TO SUMMON THE HELLHOUND FROM *INSIDE* OUR BORDERS.

IT SEEMS HADES WOULD VERY MUCH LIKE TO KILL PERCY BEFORE HE CAN CLEAR HIS FATHER'S NAME.

I DON'T PRETEND TO UNDERSTAND WHY HE HAS CHOSEN THIS MOMENT TO PIT HIS BROTHERS AGAINST ONE ANOTHER. BUT ONE THING IS CERTAIN--

--PERCY MUST GO TO THE UNDERWORLD, FIND THE MASTER BOLT, AND REVEAL THE TRUTH.

I DON'T SUPPOSE I CAN COUNT ON ANY OLYMPIAN BACKUP.

CHEW CHEW

GODS CANNOT CROSS UNINVITED INTO EACH OTHER'S DOMAINS. BUT HALF-BLOODS CAN GO ANYWHERE, AND NO GOD CAN BE HELD RESPONSIBLE FOR THEIR ACTIONS.

THE DECISION TO CLAIM YOU IS A RISKY GAMBLE, BUT POSEIDON IS DESPERATE. YOUR FATHER **NEEDS** YOU, PERCY.

IN OTHER WORDS, HE'S **USING** ME.

DO NOT JUDGE HIM TOO--

HE HAS HIS REASONS, I HAVE MINE. SO WHAT NOW? I GRAB A SHOVEL AND START **DIGGING** MY WAY TO THE UNDERWORLD?

THE UNDERWORLD, LIKE OLYMPUS, MOVES FROM AGE TO AGE. TODAY YOU'LL FIND ITS ENTRANCE AT D.O.A. RECORDING STUDIOS IN LOS ANGELES.

L.A.? OKAY, **THAT** ACTUALLY MAKES SENSE.

YOU MAY TAKE TWO COMPANIONS ON YOUR QUEST.

MR. D. HAS DECIDED TO GIVE GROVER A CHANCE TO REDEEM HIMSELF AS YOUR PROTECTOR. **IF** YOU WILL HAVE HIM.

-:GULP:-

ALL THE WAY, G-MAN.

I WON'T LET YOU DOWN.

NO TIME TO WASTE, THEN. I'VE ALREADY TAKEN THE LIBERTY OF HAVING YOUR BAGS PACKED. NOW FOLLOW ME--

"--THE THIRD MEMBER OF YOUR PARTY AWAITS."

IF YOU AND GOAT BOY ARE GOING TO SAVE THE WORLD, I'M THE BEST PERSON TO KEEP YOU FROM *MESSING UP*, SEAWEED BRAIN.

JUST TRY NOT TO, YOU KNOW, USE ME AS *BAIT* THIS TIME.

NO PROMISES.

WAIT UP!

JUST WANTED TO SAY GOOD LUCK. AND I THOUGHT MAYBE YOU COULD USE THESE.

THEY CAME IN HANDY DURING *MY* QUEST.

MAIA!

FLAP, FLAP FLAP

AWESOME!

A LOT OF HOPES ARE RIDING ON YOU, PERCY. SO JUST... KILL SOME MONSTERS FOR ME, OKAY?

I'LL DO MY BEST. AND THANKS, LUKE.

I CAN'T USE THESE, CAN I?

HE MEANT WELL, BUT TAKING TO THE AIR WOULD NOT BE WISE FOR YOU. THAT IS *ZEUS'S* DOMAIN.

HEY, GROVER! WANT SOME MAGIC SHOES?

FOR REAL?!

YOU'LL REMEMBER *THIS* ITEM FROM YOUR ENCOUNTER AT THE MUSEUM.

MAIA!

ITS NAME IS "ANAKLUSMOS."

"RIPTIDE."

THAT IS INDEED THE TRANSLATION. YOUR GREEK IS COMING ALONG NICELY.

UNCAP IT.

WHOA!

CELESTIAL BRONZE. DEADLY TO MONSTERS, BUT PERFECTLY HARMLESS TO HUMANS--THEY AREN'T IMPORTANT ENOUGH FOR THE BLADE TO KILL.

UNFORTUNATELY, HALF-BLOODS ARE TWICE AS VULNERABLE. YOU CAN BE KILLED BY EITHER CELESTIAL *OR* NORMAL WEAPONS.

GOOD TO KNOW.

MAIA!!!

CHIRON, I...

NEVER MIND THAT, CHILD. TOO MANY TIMES I'VE SAID GOODBYE TO MY CHARGES, AND I HAVE YET TO ACQUIRE A TASTE FOR IT.

THE DRIVER WILL TAKE YOU AS FAR AS THE CITY. AFTER THAT, YOU MUST VENTURE ALONE.

GODSPEED TO YOU ALL.

NOTE TO SELF: NEXT TIME WE'RE ATTACKED BY HADES'S TORTURERS, SOMEONE GRAB OUR BACKPACKS *BEFORE* WE MAKE OUR GETAWAY.

TIN CANS... I LEFT A PERFECTLY GOOD SACK OF TIN CANS.

~ZZZZZ~

I'M SORRY FOR GETTING YOU MIXED UP IN THIS DUMB QUEST. IT'S *MY FAULT* YOU'RE EVEN HERE.

PERCY, I *BEGGED* MR. D. TO BIND ME TO YOU. BRINGING YOU BACK SAFE FROM THIS QUEST IS THE ONLY WAY I'LL EVER GET MY SEARCHER'S LICENSE.

LICENSE TO SEARCH FOR WHAT?

NOT WHAT. *WHO.*

THE GREAT GOD *PAN.* LORD OF THE SATYRS AND PROTECTOR OF ALL THE WILD PLACES OF EARTH.

HE DISAPPEARED TWO THOUSAND YEARS AGO, AND EVER SINCE, THE BRAVEST SATYRS OF EACH GENERATION HAVE PLEDGED THEIR LIVES TO FINDING HIM.

MY FATHER WAS A SEARCHER...AND MY UNCLE. BUT IT'LL BE DIFFERENT FOR ME. I'LL BE THE FIRST SEARCHER TO COME BACK ALIVE.

HANG ON-- THE *FIRST*? YOU MEAN *EVERY* SATYR THAT'S GONE OFF TO FIND PAN HAS DIED... AND YOU STILL WANT TO GO?

THE BELIEF THAT HE'S OUT THERE SOMEWHERE IS ALL THAT KEEPS US SATYRS FROM DESPAIRING WHEN WE LOOK AT WHAT *HUMANS* HAVE DONE TO THE WORLD.

munch, munch

YOU'RE NOT SELFISH, PERCY.

WHAT? HOW DID--

SATYRS CAN READ EMOTIONS. THAT'S HOW I KNOW THAT YOU DIDN'T TAKE THIS QUEST TO SAVE THE WORLD. YOU TOOK IT TO GET *PAYBACK* FOR YOUR MOM.

AND IMPRESS YOUR *DAD*.

SATYRS' EMOTIONS MUST WORK *DIFFERENTLY* THAN HUMANS', BECAUSE YOU'RE ONLY HALF RIGHT. I COULDN'T CARE LESS WHAT MY *DAD* THINKS.

HE NEVER CARED ABOUT *ME*.

YOU TAKE FIRST WATCH. I'M GOING TO GET SOME SLEEP.

THE LITTLE HERO. TOO *WEAK*, TOO *YOUNG*, BUT PERHAPS YOU WILL DO.

THEY HAVE *MISLED* YOU, BOY. *BARTER* WITH ME; I WILL GIVE YOU WHAT YOU WANT.

HELP ME *RISE*, LITTLE HERO. BRING ME THE BOLT. STRIKE A *BLOW* AGAINST THE TREACHEROUS GODS.

MOM?

YES. COME *CLOSER*.

NO! WAKE!

WAKE!

WA--

--KE UP!

WE'RE ON A *QUEST*, NOT SPRING BREAK.

WHILE YOU WERE ZONKED OUT, GROVER FOUND US A WAY WEST.

MIDTOWN, YOU SAY?

GROVER, ARE YOU...UH...*TALKING* TO THAT THING?

HE'S NOT A "THING." HIS NAME IS GLADIOLA.

AND I *AM* HALF ANIMAL.

YAP! YAP!

WELL, YEAH, BUT IT'S THE *BOTTOM* HALF.

YOU'RE HOPELESS.

GLADIOLA RAN AWAY FROM A RICH LOCAL FAMILY, BUT HE'S WILLING TO LET US RETURN HIM SO WE CAN COLLECT THE REWARD.

WE'LL USE THE MONEY TO BUY OUR TICKETS TO L.A. SIMPLE.

NOT ANOTHER BUS...

NOPE. THERE'S A TRAIN STATION A HALF MILE DOWN THE LINE. GLADIOLA SAYS THE WESTBOUND TRAIN LEAVES AT NOON.

JUST EAST OF ST. LOUIS.
JUNE 13.

8 DAYS UNTIL THE SUMMER
SOLSTICE AND AN OLYMPIAN
BATTLE ROYAL ENSUES.

DID YOU...?

CENTAURS. EXCEPT FOR CHIRON, THEY'RE ALL PRETTY WILD.

I DON'T GET IT. GROVER AND MRS. DODDS WERE IN DISGUISE, OKAY, BUT HOW COME *NOBODY* NOTICES THIS OTHER STUFF?

THREE FURIES ON A BUS FULL OF PASSENGERS OUGHTA BE *FRONT-PAGE* NEWS. EVEN IN A PLACE AS WEIRD AS JERSEY.

MIST.

OBVIOUSLY IT GETS MISSED. WHAT I'M ASKING IS--

NOT "MISSED" WITH AN E-D, SEAWEED BRAIN. *"MIST."* S-T.

THE ILIAD IS FULL OF REFERENCES TO THE STUFF. WHENEVER GODS OR MONSTERS MIX WITH THE HUMAN WORLD, THEY CREATE MIST.

IT DOESN'T AFFECT HALF-BLOODS, BUT IT MAKES MORTALS SEE THINGS DIFFERENTLY THAN WE DO. KEEPS THEM FROM GOING NUTS.

OH, WELL. *MIST.* THAT MAKES *PERFECT* SENSE.

WE'VE ARRIVED AT ST. LOUIS STATION. THERE WILL BE A THREE-HOUR LAYOVER BEFORE DEPARTURE TO POINTS WEST.

WHERE ARE YOU GOING?

IT'S BEEN FIVE YEARS SINCE I'VE BEEN OUTSIDE CAMP, SO I SAY WE DO SOME *SIGHTSEEING.*

WAKE UP GOAT BOY AND FOLLOW ME.

ARCHES ARE *BEAUTIFUL* IN THEIR SIMPLICITY, AREN'T THEY?

OF COURSE, I WOULD'VE MADE THE WINDOWS ON THIS ONE LARGER.

AND PROBABLY ADDED A SEE-THROUGH FLOOR.

IT'S NOT LIKE THE *TENSILE STRENGTH* OF THESE BUILDING MATERIALS CAN'T SUPPORT IT.

IF YOU SAY SO...

I *DO* SAY SO. ARCHITECTURE IS SORT OF A HOBBY OF MINE. SOMEDAY I'M GOING TO BUILD MONUMENTS LIKE THIS. BUT *BETTER*.

THE OBSERVATION DECK WILL BE CLOSING IN FIVE MINUTES.

PLEASE MAKE YOUR WAY TO THE ELEVATORS AT EITHER SIDE OF THE ROOM.

BOTH CARS ARE FULL. YOU'LL HAVE TO WAIT FOR THE NEXT ONE.

OH! NO PROBLEM AT ALL, SIR!

VERY WELL, SONNY. IF YOU *INSIST*.

AND *I* AM HIS FAMILY. I AM ECHIDNA, THE *MOTHER* OF *MONSTERS*.

CHIMERA. IT'S AN EASY MISTAKE TO MAKE.

SONNY? IS THAT YOUR CHIHUAHUA'S NAME?

I DON'T SUPPOSE HE HAS ANY *PINK POODLES* IN HIS FAMILY...

NOT *CHIHUAHUA*, GODLING.

RRRRRR

GRRRR

STAY BACK!

YAAA!

SWAT!

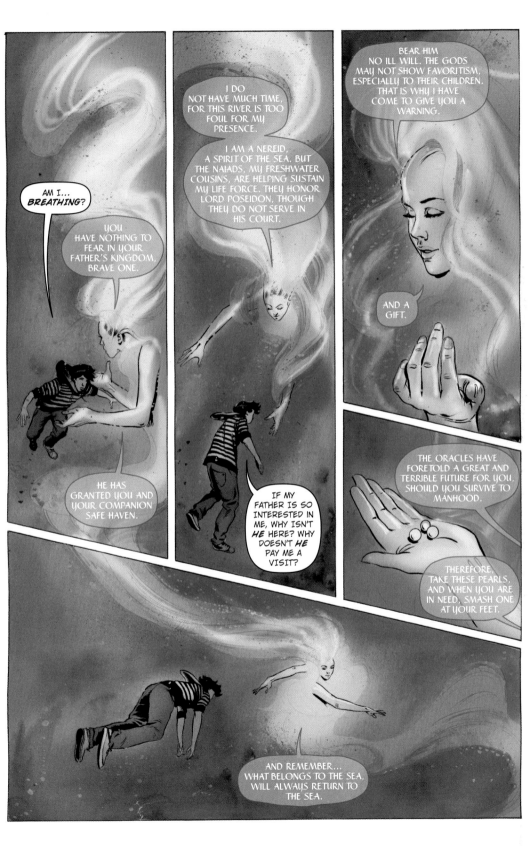

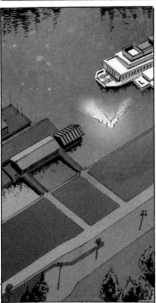

WE CAN'T LEAVE YOU ALONE FOR FIVE MINUTES! WHAT HAPPENED?

I RAN INTO A CHIMERA AND HIS MOMMY, AND THEN I JUMPED.

YOU KNOW, TYPICAL *SIGHTSEEING* STUFF.

NOT THAT I'M UNAPPRECIATIVE, BUT DO YOU THINK NEXT TIME YOUR DAD CAN KEEP *ME* DRY, TOO?

FORGET ABOUT THAT. THIS PLACE IS CRAWLING WITH COPS... PROBABLY MONSTERS, TOO. LET'S GET BACK TO THE TRAIN.

DO YOU ACCEPT THE CHARGES?

UM...YES?

PLEASE HOLD.

PERCY!

SORRY ABOUT CALLING COLLECT, BUT I DIDN'T KNOW WHERE YOU WERE. JUST DON'T FORGET TO PAY THE BILL -- IRIS HAS BEEN KNOWN TO CUT PEOPLE'S SERVICE.

LUKE? WHAT IS THIS? WHO'S IRIS?

THE GODDESS OF RAINBOWS. SHE CARRIES MESSAGES FOR US SOMETIMES. CELL PHONES ARE TOO EASY FOR MONSTERS TO TRACK.

SO WHAT'S YOUR PROGRESS? WORD LEAKED OUT BACK HERE ABOUT THE ZEUS-POSEIDON STANDOFF, AND IT'S SHAPING UP TO BE THE TROJAN WAR ALL OVER AGAIN. THE CAMPERS ARE AT EACH OTHERS' THROATS.

WE'RE IN DENVER. NOT TOO BAD, CONSIDERING. CHIMERAS AND FURIES AND ANNABETH, OH MY...

ARE YOU WEARING THE FLYING SHOES? I'LL FEEL BETTER IF I KNOW THEY'VE DONE YOU SOME GOOD.

OH...UH, YEAH! THEY FIT LIKE GLOVES... ER, FOR MY FEET.

WISH I COULD DO MORE, YOU GUYS GOING TO THE UNDERWORLD AND ALL.

I DON'T CARE WHAT CHIRON SAYS--

--I JUST KNOW HADES IS THE THIEF. HIS HELM OF DARKNESS LETS HIM MELT INTO SHADOW, AND YOU'D HAVE TO BE INVISIBLE TO SWIPE THE MASTER BOLT FROM UNDER ZEUS'S NOSE.

ANYWAY, I SHOULD GET GOING. SOUNDS LIKE SOME OF THE CAMPERS ARE FIGHTING AGAIN.

HANG TOUGH, PERCY. YOU'LL GET THERE, I KNOW YOU WILL. AND TELL GROVER IT'LL BE BETTER THIS TIME.

FSSHH-T.

WE'RE IN LUCK. GOAT BOY AND I PANHANDLED ENOUGH TO GET A CHEESEBURGER AND FRIES AT THE DINER DOWN THE STREET.

A CHEESEBURGER EACH?

-:HMPH:- TRY TOTAL.

HEY! WAIT UP! GROVER CAN HAVE THE FRIES, BUT HALF OF THAT CHEESEBURGER HAS MY NAME ON IT!

->SCARF<-

->CHOMP<-

->MMPF<-

YOU BIG SPENDERS READY FOR YOUR CHECK?

SET 'EM UP AGAIN, DOLL.

MY TREAT.

R-RIGHT AWAY, SIR.

SO YOU'RE THE WATERBOY, HUH? HEARD YOU BUSTED CLARISSE'S SPEAR.

SO WHAT? YOU COME HERE LOOKING TO GET SOMETHING OF YOURS BUSTED?

UH, PERCY...? BE CAREFUL. HIS AURA PROVOKES AGGRESSION IN ANYONE NEAR HIM.

IT'S COOL. I DON'T SWEAT A LITTLE 'TUDE, LONG AS EVERYONE KNOWS WHO THE **BOSS** IS. YOU **DO** KNOW WHO I AM, DON'T YOU, PUNK?

YOU'RE ARES, CLARISSE'S DAD. MY CONDOLENCES.

WHO'D YOU MATE WITH TO GET HER? A CROCODILE?

HEH HEH HEH. A REAL CHIP OFF THE OLD CORAL, AIN'T YOU?

ME AND YOUR OLD MAN GO WAY BACK, YOU KNOW. THAT'S WHY I'M HERE--HEARD YOU WERE IN TOWN, AND I KNEW YOU'D NEED AN ASSIST.

WE'RE DOING FINE ON OUR OWN.

THEY MUST'VE BROUGHT YOU ALONG FOR YOUR **LOOKS**, PRINCESS, 'CUZ YOU SURE MISSED OUT ON **MAMA'S BRAINS**.

NO MONEY PLUS NO WHEELS AND NO CLUE EQUALS **NO CHANCE**.

YOU AIN'T THE FIRST TO GO HUNTING FOR ZEUS'S TOY. WHEN IT FIRST GOT SNATCHED, HE SENT HIS BEST TO TRACK IT DOWN. APOLLO, ARTEMIS...AND ME, OF COURSE.

IF **I** COULDN'T SNIFF OUT A WEAPON THAT POWERFUL...

AN ARMY MARCHES ON ITS STOMACH, SO CHOW DOWN, KIDDIES. I'LL BE WAITING OUTSIDE.

REVEILLE, TROOPERS. TIME'S A-WASTIN', AND THERE'S A *LONG* ROAD AHEAD.

--YOU'LL HAVE TO SETTLE FOR *STOWAWAY SERVICE.*

HERE'S SOME CASH AND SUPPLIES. AS FOR A RIDE WEST--

BETTER DUCK INSIDE BEFORE THE DRIVER FINISHES HIS LUNCH.

WHY ALL OF THE HELP?

LIKE I SAID, ME AND YOUR OLD MAN GO WAY BACK.

I'M THE ONE WHO TOLD HIM ABOUT HADES STEALING THE BOLT.

FRAMING SOMEBODY TO START A WAR--*OLDEST TRICK* IN THE BOOK.

IN A WAY, YOU GOT ME TO THANK FOR YOUR LITTLE QUEST.

WHICH REMINDS ME: WHAT A SOLDIER NEEDS MORE THAN ANYTHING TO COMPLETE HIS MISSION IS *MOTIVATION.* SO WHEN YOU THINK ABOUT QUITTING, REMEMBER THIS--

--YOUR *MOM* AIN'T DEAD. SHE'S BEING *HELD HOSTAGE.* TAKING SOMEBODY TO CONTROL SOMEBODY ELSE--THAT'S ANOTHER OLDIE BUT GOODIE.

MOUNT UP, PUNKS.

BRUMBLLBBB

CLICK

UM... *DEUS EX MACHINA,* ANYONE?

WHOA...

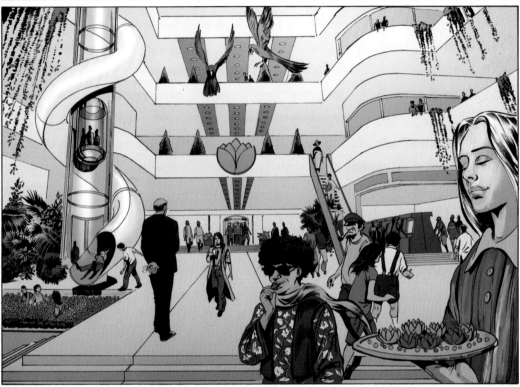

AH, **WELCOME** TO THE LOTUS RESORT AND CASINO. WE'RE **SO GLAD** YOU'VE BOOKED YOUR STAY WITH US.

WHAT? I THINK YOU'VE MADE A MISTAKE.

INDEED WE HAVE. YOUR ROOM ISN'T QUITE READY, I'M AFRAID.

PLEASE ACCEPT THESE LOTUS CARDS, ON THE HOUSE. YOU CAN REDEEM THEM ANYWHERE IN THE BUILDING. GOOD AS CASH.

BUT--

YOU REMEMBER THE TRAVEL AGENT TELLING US ABOUT THE LOTUS CARDS, DON'T YOU? WE CAN USE THEM TO BUY **FOOD** OR **CLOTHES** OR...

YOU'LL COME FIND US WHEN THE ROOM IS READY?

IT IS MY **TOP** PRIORITY.

beep

bloop

wee-on

blip

THIS IS THE BEST GAME *EVER!* I'VE ALREADY MASTERED THE SKYSCRAPER LEVEL!

URBAN PLANNER EXTREME

"URBAN PLANNER EXTREME"? SOUNDS LIKE A *HOMEWORK* ASSIGNMENT.

RESCUE MOM

HEY, KID, YOU KNOW HOW TO PLAY THIS ONE?

"RESCUE MOM" SAYS IT ALL, CHIEF.

SO I PLAY THE PART OF A PARAMEDIC WITH KIDS?

NO, LIKE, YOU HAVE TO *RESCUE* YOUR *MOM.*

FROM WHAT?

HOW SHOULD I KNOW, CHIEF? IT'S YOUR GAME.

IT'S MY GAME...

ANNABETH? SOMETHING IS WRONG HERE...

YOU'RE TELLING ME. IF I DON'T GET THIS FREEWAY BUILT, THE *GRIDLOCK* IS GOING TO CHASE POTENTIAL DEVELOPERS AWAY FROM DOWNTOWN.

NO. I MEAN SOMETHING IS WRONG WITH THIS *PLACE.*

DOESN'T IT SEEM STRANGE THAT THERE'S A GAME ALL ABOUT URBAN PLANNING? LIKE IT WAS MADE JUST FOR YOU.

I'LL HAVE YOU KNOW, *PLENTY* OF KIDS ENJOY PLAYING GAMES THAT REQUIRE THOUGHT. *PRESENT COMPANY* EXCLUDED.

ANNABETH! STOP!

HEY! NOW I'M GOING TO HAVE TO START OVER AT--

WHAT WOULD *ATHENA* DO?

WHERE'S GROVER?

EAT *LEAD*, LITTERBUG!

POLLUTER SHOOTER

WHA--?

POLLUTER SHOOTER

LEMME GO! DON'T YOU SEE WHAT THEY'RE DOING TO THE FOREST?!

LEAVING SO SOON?

HOW ABOUT WE UPGRADE YOUR ROOM TO AN *EXECUTIVE SUITE*?

ON THE HOUSE!

CAN IT, BUDDY.

FREE UPGRADE!

I THOUGHT IT WAS NIGHTTIME. HOW MANY HOURS WERE WE IN THERE?

UH, GUYS...? WE WEREN'T IN THERE FOR HOURS--

--TRY DAYS.

STILL LAS VEGAS. JUNE 20.

1 DAY UNTIL THE SUMMER SOLSTICE, AND 250 MILES TO GO. NOT MUCH TIME!

HOW FAST CAN YOU GET US TO L.A.?

DEPENDS ON HOW MUCH YOU'RE GONNA PAY ME.

DO YOU TAKE CASINO CARDS?

ONLY IF THEY'RE GOOD.

SWIPE!

CHING!

SKREEECH!

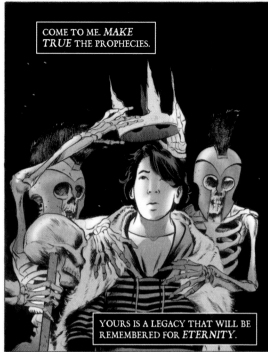

COME TO ME. *MAKE TRUE* THE PROPHECIES.

YOURS IS A LEGACY THAT WILL BE REMEMBERED FOR *ETERNITY*.

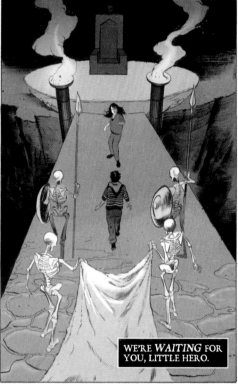

WE'RE *WAITING* FOR YOU, LITTLE HERO.

HAIL, THE CONQUERING HERO!

-:*GASP!*:-

PERCY! WE MADE IT TO L.A. IN UNDER THREE HOURS-- GREAT TIME!

YOU OKAY?

YEAH... I'M GOOD.

LOS ANGELES.
JUNE 20.

DOA
RECORDING STUDIOS

ONE DAY UNTIL THE SUMMER SOLSTICE AND THE END OF THE WORLD AS WE KNOW IT.

WHAT'D THEY SAY IN THE OLD DAYS? ROCK 'N' ROLL IS THE ROAD TO HELL?

TECHNICALLY, IT ISN'T HELL. IT'S ONLY THE *UNDERWORLD.* HOW BAD CAN IT BE?

NO MATCH FOR A TRIO LIKE *US,* RIGHT?

SURE. LISTEN, PERCY, BEFORE WE GO INSIDE...THERE'S SOMETHING I SHOULD'VE TOLD YOU FROM THE BEGINNING.

CHIRON'S STORY ABOUT THALIA AND THE PINE TREE...*I* WAS THE SATYR WHO WAS SUPPOSED TO PROTECT HER.

I GOT HER *KILLED,* SAME AS I ALMOST DID YOU.

ANYWAY, I JUST THOUGHT YOU SHOULD KNOW...SO YOU WOULDN'T COUNT ON ME TOO MUCH.

THALIA WASN'T YOUR FAULT. *LUKE* AND *I* WERE THERE, TOO, REMEMBER?

WE WEREN'T YOUR RESPONSIBILITY. YOU COULD'VE LEFT US BEHIND AND GOTTEN HER TO CAMP LIKE YOU WERE TOLD. BUT YOU *HELPED* US.

I WOULDN'T BE HERE IF IT WEREN'T FOR YOU.

I DON'T KNOW WHAT HAPPENED WITH THALIA, BUT I *DO* KNOW YOU'VE GOT THE BIGGEST HEART OF ANY SATYR *EVER.* THERE'S *NOBODY* I'D RATHER HAVE AT MY SIDE.

NOW LET'S SHOW THESE CALIFORNIANS HOW WE DO THINGS *NEW YORK* STYLE.

YOUR NAME IS *CHIRON*?

CHARON

IT'S *CHAR*ON, MATE.

AND YOU'D BE WISE NOT TO CONFUSE ME WITH THAT POMPOUS, *FOUR-LEGGED--*

SAY...HAVE TROUBLE READING, DO YOU?

-:HMPH:-

YOU'RE A GODLING. AND A *NOT-DEAD* ONE, AT THAT. PITY.

WE WANT TO GO TO THE UNDERWORLD.

WELL, *THAT'S* REFRESHING. USUALLY I GET "THERE MUST BE A MISTAKE, MR. CHARON," OR "I'M NOT SUPPOSED TO BE DEAD, MR. CHARON."

NEVERTHELESS, I MUST DECLINE.

CHARON

C'MON. STUCK IN HERE FOR ALL ETERNITY OR NOT, EVEN *YOU* MUST KNOW THAT HADES IS GUNNING FOR HALF-BLOODS.

WHAT'S HE GOING TO THINK IF HE HEARS YOU TURNED US AWAY AT THE DOOR?

YOU LET US *IN*, THOUGH, AND HE MIGHT SHOW YOU SOME FAVOR.

THERE MAY EVEN BE A *RAISE* IN IT FOR YOU. WHEN'S THE LAST TIME YOU GOT A RAISE?

PLEASE, MATE. I GET PAID *TWO DRACHMAS* A HEAD, JUST LIKE ALWAYS.

AND A DRACHMA DOESN'T GO AS FAR AS IT *USED* TO, LET ME TELL YOU.

YOU MAKE A VALID POINT ABOUT THE RAISE, MATE. COME ALONG.

MR. CHARON, SIR? HOW MUCH LONGER WILL I HAVE TO WAIT?

AS LONG AS IT TAKES, *PLUS* A THOUSAND YEARS.

BECAUSE YOU *ASKED*.

THE BOAT'S ALMOST FULL ANYWAY. MAY AS WELL ADD YOU LOT AND SHOVE OFF.

GOING *DOWN*.

WH-WHAT'S HAPPENING?

IT DOESN'T *FEEL* LIKE WE'RE GOING DOWN!

MORE LIKE *FORWARD!*

ELEVATORS DON'T FLOAT.

YOU NEED A FERRY--

--TO CROSS THE *RIVER STYX.*

OFF YOU GO, MATE. I ONLY TAKE PASSENGERS *ONE WAY*.

I'D WISH YOU LUCK--

--BUT THERE *ISN'T ANY* DOWN HERE.

NOW WHAT?

FOLLOW THE CROWD, I GUESS.

THE FIELDS OF ASPHODEL.

DI IMMORTALES...

THERE ARE SO *MANY*...WHAT ARE THEY DOING?

THE ONLY THING THEY *CAN* DO: STAND AROUND. FOREVER.

GUYS, LOOK.

HADES'S HOME ADDRESS.

GROVER! WHERE ARE YOU?!

OVER HERE!

THESE SHOES HAVE A *MIND OF THEIR OWN!*

ANNABETH! UNTIE THE LACES!

I'M TRYING!

GET THEM OFF!

FLAP
FLAP
FLAP

THERE IT GOES!

ONE... MORE...

HURRY! I'M SLIPPING!

FLAP
FLAP
FLAP

GOT IT!

WHAT WAS *THAT* ALL ABOUT?!

I'M PRETTY SURE THAT'S THE ENTRANCE TO *TARTARUS*. RESERVED FOR THE REALLY, *REALLY* BAD BADDIES. IT'S FOR WHEN THE FIELDS OF PUNISHMENT JUST AREN'T PUNISHMENT ENOUGH.

BUT WHAT WOULD IT WANT WITH GROVER...?

ME? DON'T LOOK AT *ME*! I'M A *VEGETARIAN*.

HE'S RIGHT. MAYBE WHATEVER IS DOWN THERE ISN'T AFTER HIM.

I COULD SWEAR I'VE DREAMED ABOUT THIS PIT...

~GROAN~ OUT OF THE FRYING PAN, INTO THE *FIRE*.

THIS PIT? YOU'VE DREAMED ABOUT *THIS* PIT?

I'M NOT SURE WHAT THAT MEANS, BUT I DON'T WANT TO STAND HERE WHILE WE FIGURE IT OUT.

I'M WITH YOU.

THE *QUICKER* WE GET THE BOLT AND GET OUT OF HERE, THE BETTER.

LET'S GO FIND HADES.

MAY WE... UM...TALK TO YOUR BOSS?

PLEASE?

THAT'S AS CLOSE AS WE'RE GOING TO GET TO AN INVITATION.

YOU ARE BRAVE TO COME HERE, *SON OF POSEIDON*, AFTER WHAT YOU HAVE DONE TO ME.

OR PERHAPS YOU ARE MERELY *FOOLISH*.

LORD AND UNCLE, I COME TO YOU WITH TWO REQUESTS.

ARROGANT CHILD. AS IF YOU HAVE NOT ALREADY TAKEN ENOUGH, NOW YOU WOULD ASK FOR MORE.

SPEAK, THEN, WHILE I PONDER IN WHAT *MANNER* I WISH FOR YOU TO DIE.

THERE CAN'T BE A WAR AMONG THE GODS, UNCLE.

IT WOULD BE KIND OF...BAD. LET ME RETURN THE MASTER BOLT TO OLYMPUS, AND I'LL END THIS.

THERE MUST BE OTHER WAYS TO GROW YOUR KINGDOM.

WHY WOULD I *WANT* WAR, GODLING? FOR MY *KINGDOM*?

THE DEAD WILL COME TO ME WITHOUT INTERVENTION.

DID YOU NOT SEE THE SPRAWL OF THE ASPHODEL FIELDS?

IT IS *I* WHO HAS BEEN WRONGED.

BUT YOU STOLE ZEUS'S BOLT--

LIES! YOUR FATHER MAY FOOL ZEUS, BOY, BUT I AM NOT SO STUPID. I SEE HIS PLAN.

WAIT...YOUR HELM IS MISSING, TOO? THERE MUST BE SOME MISTAKE...

A *MISTAKE*? OPEN YOUR PACK, THEN, AND WE WILL *SEE* WHO IS MISTAKEN.

IT WAS *YOU* WHO PILFERED THE BOLT, AS WELL AS MY *HELM OF DARKNESS*.

HAD I NOT SENT MY FURY TO YANCY ACADEMY, POSEIDON MIGHT HAVE SUCCEEDED IN HIS *SCHEME* TO START A WAR.

YOUR FATHER CANNOT *BLACKMAIL* ME INTO SUPPORTING HIM. I WILL HAVE MY HELM *BACK!*

YOU KNOW, I'M GETTING *REALLY TIRED* OF PEOPLE CALLING ME A--

--THIEF?

I DON'T UNDERSTAND. HOW...?

DO NOT ATTEMPT TO *DISGUISE* YOUR PURPOSE. I KNEW IF I WAS PATIENT, YOU WOULD COME TO BARGAIN WITH ME.

TO BARGAIN FOR *HER*.

SHE IS NOT DEAD. NOT *YET*. I WILL RELEASE HER IF YOU RETURN MY HELM. YOU CAN ALSO LEAVE *THE BOLT* AS PAYMENT FOR THE INSULT THAT HAS BEEN DONE TO ME.

PERCY...? ARE YOU THINKING WHAT I'M THINKING?

WE'VE BEEN **SET UP.**

SO WHAT DO WE DO **NOW**?

I MIGHT HAVE AN IDEA...

GOOD, BECAUSE I **DON'T.**

AH, YES, **THE PEARLS.** HOW MY BROTHER LOVES HIS LITTLE TRICKS.

BUT THERE ARE ONLY **THREE.** WHICH OF YOUR FRIENDS WILL YOU TRADE FOR YOUR MOTHER?

OR WILL YOU TRADE **YOURSELF?**

I'M SORRY, MOM. I'LL FIND A WAY, I PROMISE.

WHAT ARE YOU--?

PERSEUS JACKSON, YOU **WILL NOT** DEFY ME.

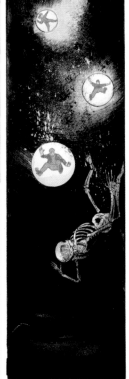

LOS ANGELES.
JUNE 21.

MERE HOURS
UNTIL THE SUMMER
SOLSTICE DEADLINE.

HOW'D
WE END UP
HERE?

"WHAT BELONGS
TO THE SEA, WILL
ALWAYS RETURN
TO THE SEA."

-:COUGH
COUGH:-

BUT
DOES ANYONE
KNOW WHAT'S
GOING ON?

HADES
ISN'T EVEN THE THIEF!
WE CAME ALL THIS WAY
FOR NOTHING!

SOMEONE ELSE SWIPED
THE MASTER BOLT--AND HADES'S
HELM--AND FRAMED ME BECAUSE I'M
POSEIDON'S NEVER-SHOULD'VE-
BEEN-BORN KID.

GEE,
I WONDER.

POSEIDON
WILL TAKE THE RAP
FOR EVERYTHING, AND
BY SUNDOWN TODAY ALL
THREE BROTHERS WILL
BE AT WAR.

BUT
WHO'D BE THAT
SNEAKY?

-:COUGH:-

WHO WANTS
WAR THAT
BAD?

BRUMBLLBB

THE BACKPACK IS SOME KIND OF MAGIC ITEM, IS THAT IT? WHEN I GOT TO HADES'S PALACE, THE BOLT MATERIALIZED INSIDE. AND I WAS CAUGHT RED-HANDED.

BUT WHY NOT KEEP THE BOLT FOR *YOURSELF*?

HADES WOULD'VE KILLED ME ANYWAY, SO WHY SEND IT TO HIM?

WHY DIDN'T I KEEP...? YEAH... WITH THAT KIND OF FIREPOWER...

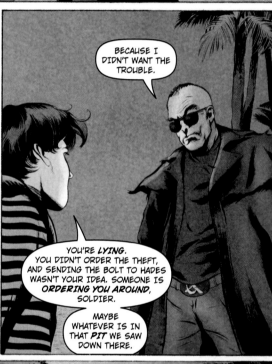

BECAUSE I DIDN'T WANT THE TROUBLE.

YOU'RE *LYING*. YOU DIDN'T ORDER THE THEFT, AND SENDING THE BOLT TO HADES WASN'T YOUR IDEA. SOMEONE IS *ORDERING YOU AROUND*, SOLDIER.

MAYBE WHATEVER IS IN THAT *PIT* WE SAW DOWN THERE.

I'M THE *GOD OF WAR*!

I TAKE ORDERS FROM *NO ONE*!

RAARRGH!

SLICE

I WIN.

SOON, GODLING, YOU'LL RAISE YOUR BLADE IN BATTLE AND FEEL MY *CURSE*.

THAT SHADOW...WHAT WAS THAT?

WHO CARES? TALK ABOUT *MAKING WAVES*! PERCY, THAT WAS *AWESOME*!

WE WITNESSED THE FIGHT. SO IT TRULY WAS NOT YOU WHO STOLE THE HELM? THAT IS UNFORTUNATE. I LOOKED FORWARD TO BRINGING YOU BACK TO LORD HADES IN PIECES.

RETURN THIS TO MY UNCLE. TELL HIM THERE'S NO REASON TO GO TO WAR.

HADES ISN'T THE ONLY GOD YOU SHOULD BE WORRYING ABOUT.

YOU NEED TO BE IN NEW YORK, AND FAST. LIKE *AIRPLANE* FAST. I SURE HOPE ZEUS GIVES YOU A PASS....

WE CAN'T AFFORD PLANE TICKETS. WE'RE TAPPED.

UM... MRS. DODDS, MA'AM?

DOES THAT HELM COME WITH A FINDER'S FEE?

MANHATTAN.
JUNE 21.

"PAY ATTENTION, PERCY. WHEN YOU GET TO NEW YORK, HERE'S WHAT YOU DO:

"FIRST, TAKE A CAB TO THE EMPIRE STATE BUILDING.

"TELL THE GUARD AT THE DESK THAT YOU WANT TO TAKE THE ELEVATOR TO THE *SIX HUNDREDTH* FLOOR.

"HE'LL INSIST THERE ARE ONLY *ONE HUNDRED* AND *TWO* FLOORS--

"--SO FIND A WAY TO CONVINCE HIM TO LET YOU THROUGH.

"PUT THE KEY CARD HE GIVES YOU INTO THE SLOT IN THE ELEVATOR.

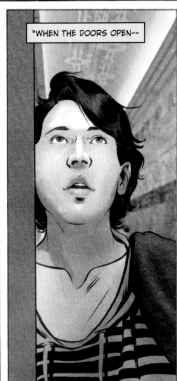

"WHEN THE DOORS OPEN--

"ZEUS AND POSEIDON WILL BE IN THE PALACE AT THE SUMMIT."

YOU *DARE* TO FLY THROUGH MY DOMAIN. I SHOULD HAVE *BLASTED* YOU FROM THE *SKY* FOR YOUR IMPUDENCE.

AND RISK DESTROYING YOUR PRIZED BOLT? LET US HEAR HIM OUT, BROTHER.

I BROUGHT THIS, UNCLE, EVEN THOUGH I'M NOT THE ONE WHO STOLE IT. IT WAS ARES, WITH HELP FROM SOMEONE INSIDE CAMP HALF-BLOOD.

I SENSE THAT YOU SPEAK THE TRUTH. BUT FOR ARES TO DO SUCH A THING...IT IS MOST UNLIKE HIM.

HE IS PROUD AND IMPULSIVE. IT RUNS IN THE FAMILY.

I DON'T THINK IT WAS HIM. I MEAN, NOT EXACTLY. SOMEONE ELSE--SOME*THING* ELSE-- WAS CONTROLLING HIM.

AFTER I BEAT HIM ON THE BEACH, THERE WAS THIS PRESENCE...SOME WEIRD SHADOW. IT REMINDED ME OF DREAMS I'VE BEEN HAVING, ABOUT A VOICE COMING FROM A PIT--

--A PIT THAT WE SAW IN THE UNDERWORLD.

IT WAS THE ENTRANCE TO TARTARUS. SOMETHING *POWERFUL* AND *EVIL* IS STIRRING DOWN THERE...SOMETHING EVEN OLDER THAN THE GODS.

WE WILL SPEAK NO MORE OF THIS.

I MUST GO AND PURIFY THIS BOLT IN THE WATERS OF LEMNOS, TO REMOVE THE HUMAN TAINT FROM ITS METAL.

YOU HAVE DONE ME A SERVICE, BOY. TO SHOW MY THANKS, I SHALL *SPARE* YOUR LIFE.

BUT I DO NOT TRUST YOU, PERSEUS JACKSON. YOU ARE YOUR FATHER'S *WRONGDOING*, AND I WORRY WHAT YOUR ARRIVAL BODES FOR THE FUTURE.

AH, BROTHER. YOU ALWAYS WERE ONE FOR DRAMATIC EXITS.

FATHER... I MEAN, SIR? IT'S *KRONOS*, ISN'T IT?

DOWN IN THAT PIT. THE VOICE I HEARD IN MY DREAMS.

IT'S THE KING OF THE TITANS.

I FEAR THAT IT MAY BE INDEED. IN THE FIRST WAR, ZEUS CUT OUR FATHER INTO A THOUSAND PIECES AND CAST HIS REMAINS INTO THE DARKEST PIT OF TARTARUS.

AND YET *TITANS* CANNOT DIE, NO MORE THAN WE GODS CAN.

WHATEVER REMAINS OF KRONOS IS STILL *ALIVE* IN SOME HIDEOUS WAY, STILL CONSCIOUS IN HIS ETERNAL PAIN. STILL *HUNGERING FOR POWER*.

HE'S HEALING. KRONOS IS *COMING BACK*.

KRONOS *DOES* STIR FROM TIME TO TIME-- TO ENTER MEN'S NIGHTMARES AND BREATHE EVIL THOUGHTS, TO AWAKEN RESTLESS MONSTERS.

BUT TO SUGGEST HE COULD *RISE FROM THE PIT*...

ZEUS HAS CLOSED DISCUSSION ON THE MATTER OF KRONOS. YOU HAVE COMPLETED YOUR QUEST, AND THAT IS ALL YOU NEED DO.

BUT YOU *CAN'T*--

I MEAN... IF YOU SAY SO, FATHER.

OBEDIENCE DOES NOT COME NATURALLY TO YOU. I MUST TAKE SOME BLAME FOR THAT, I SUPPOSE. *THE SEA* DOES NOT LIKE TO BE RESTRAINED.

YOU MUST GO NOW. ZEUS WOULD NOT BE PLEASED TO FIND YOU LINGERING HERE WHEN HE RETURNS.

RIGHT. WOULDN'T WANT TO REMIND HIM OF YOUR *WRONGDOING.*

PERCY...

I *AM* SORRY YOU WERE BORN. I HAVE BROUGHT YOU A *HERO'S FATE,* AND A HERO'S FATE IS NEVER ANYTHING BUT TRAGIC.

MOST OF ALL, I AM SORRY THAT OUR LAWS *FORBID ME* FROM TREATING YOU AS A FATHER SHOULD HIS CHILD.

BUT YOU HAVE DONE WELL TODAY. WHATEVER ELSE YOU DO, KNOW THAT YOU ARE MINE. YOU ARE A *TRUE SON* OF THE SEA GOD.

OF THAT, I SHALL *ALWAYS* BE PROUD.

CAMP HALF-BLOOD. JUNE 22.

FELLOW CAMPERS, I PRESENT TO YOU GROVER UNDERWOOD, ANNABETH CHASE, AND PERCY JACKSON!

LET US APPLAUD THEM, FOR THEY HAVE DONE US *ALL* PROUD!

YEAH!

WAY TO GO!

HOORAY!

-:HUMPF:-

SO THE LITTLE *BRATS* DIDN'T GET THEMSELVES KILLED, AND NOW THEY'LL HAVE EVEN *BIGGER* EGOS. *HUZZAH.*

I GOTTA SAY, I HALF THOUGHT ZEUS WOULD *BLAST YOUR PLANE* TO SMITHEREENS.

ADMIT IT, YOU'RE *GLAD* TO SEE ME STILL IN ONE PIECE.

IN YOUR *DREAMS,* SEAWEED BRAIN.

LET THE FEAST OF CELEBRATION BEGIN!

THE HEPHAESTUS KIDS *REALLY* KNOW HOW TO PUT ON A FIREWORKS SHOW.

THERE IS GOOD CAUSE TO BE FESTIVE. IF YOU PAID ATTENTION TO MY LECTURES, THEN YOU WILL REMEMBER THAT HEROES *RARELY* ACHIEVE YOUR LEVEL OF ACCOMPLISHMENT.

AND YOU ARE STILL *QUITE YOUNG.*

WE DID ALL RIGHT, DIDN'T WE?

ALL RIGHT?!

THE COUNCIL OF CLOVEN ELDERS SAID *MY PERFORMANCE* WAS BRAVE TO THE POINT OF INDIGESTION. *HORNS AND WHISKERS* ABOVE ANYTHING THEY'VE SEEN IN THE PAST.

I'M TO BEGIN MY *SEARCH FOR PAN* RIGHT AWAY!

DON'T FORGET TO PRACTICE YOUR REED PIPES, AND MAKE SURE YOU BRING ENOUGH TIN CANS, AND--

JEEZ, ANNABETH. YOU'RE WORSE THAN AN OLD NANNY GOAT!

CONGRATS, PAL. YOU'LL BE THE ONE TO FIND PAN, I'M SURE OF IT.

IT'S GOOD TO KNOW AT LEAST *ONE OF US* GOT WHAT THEY WANTED OUT OF THIS QUEST.

AW, PERCY... I'M SORRY ABOUT YOUR MOM.

AND HERE I AM *GLOATING*...

IT'S OKAY. I'M HAPPY FOR YOU. REALLY.

HEY, WHERE'S LUKE? I'D LIKE TO SWAP *QUEST STORIES* WITH HIM, NOW THAT I HAVE SOME OF MY OWN.

WHAT'D I SAY?

PERCY... ABOUT LUKE...

"PERHAPS IT WOULD BE BEST IF YOU AND I SPOKE ALONE."

NO ONE HAS SEEN LUKE SINCE HE WAS TOLD OF YOUR QUEST'S SUCCESS. HE FLED CAMP WITHOUT EXPLANATION.

I AM AFRAID THAT LEAVES US WITH BUT *ONE CONCLUSION.*

WHY? OF ALL THE PEOPLE...ARE YOU *SURE?*

REMEMBER, PERCY, THE SHOES THAT PULLED GROVER TO THE EDGE OF TARTARUS... *YOU* WERE THEIR INTENDED WEARER.

IT SEEMS *LUKE* WAS THE THIEF OF THE SYMBOLS OF POWER. RARELY HAVE THE TALENTS OF A *DIVINE BLOODLINE* BEEN PUT TO SUCH NEFARIOUS ENDS.

HE MUST HAVE SUMMONED THE *HELLHOUND* THAT DAY AT THE CREEK AS WELL. PERHAPS TO MAKE US BELIEVE YOU WERE UNSAFE HERE, SO WE WOULD SEND YOU AWAY.

AS FOR HIS MOTIVES, IT IS DIFFICULT TO SAY....LUKE HAS ALWAYS BEEN A TROUBLED BOY, IN PART BECAUSE OF HIS ESTRANGEMENT FROM HIS FATHER.

A MIND IN SUCH A STATE IS FERTILE GROUND. A POWER AS STRONG AS KRONOS CAN SOW WICKED CROPS.

THE ORACLE WARNED I'D BE BETRAYED BY ONE WHO CALLS ME FRIEND--

--WHEN I UNZIPPED THE BACKPACK IN THE UNDERWORLD, I WAS SURE IT WAS ARES.

HE *PRETENDED* TO HELP, BUT HE WAS TRYING TO GET ME KILLED ALL ALONG.

MMM. ARES WAS "THE GOD WHO HAS TURNED." I MISTOOK THOSE WORDS TO BE IN REFERENCE TO HADES.

AS I SAID, THE ORACLE'S PROPHECIES ARE NOT ALWAYS CLEAR UNTIL EVENTS COME TO PASS.

THERE WAS **ONE LINE** FROM THE PROPHECY I DIDN'T TELL YOU ABOUT, THOUGH: "YOU SHALL FAIL TO SAVE WHAT MATTERS MOST IN THE END."

THE MEANING OF THAT ONE IS **CRYSTAL** CLEAR.

IS IT? PERHAPS THE ORACLE MEANT THAT YOU COULD NOT SAVE YOUR MOTHER, BECAUSE SHE MUST SAVE HERSELF. AND I DON'T MEAN FROM HADES.

WHETHER TO LEAVE YOUR STEPFATHER, WHETHER TO PURSUE HER OWN DREAMS...**SHE ALONE** MUST FIND THE COURAGE TO MAKE THOSE CHOICES.

SOMETHING TELLS ME SHE **ALREADY HAS**.

WHAT? HOW DO YOU--?

RETURNING THE HELM GAINED YOU FAVOR. EVEN THE **LORD OF THE DEAD** PAYS HIS DEBTS.

MOM!

END OF BOOK 1.

Adapted from the novel
Percy Jackson & the Olympians, Book One: The Lightning Thief

Text copyright © 2010 by Rick Riordan
Illustrations copyright © 2010 Disney Enterprises, Inc.

Design by Jim Titus
Edited by Christian Trimmer

Printed in the United States of America
FAC-038091-20356
First Edition, October 2010
17
ISBN 978-1-4231-1696-7 (hardcover)

ISBN 978-1-4231-1710-0 (paperback)
Library of Congress Control Number For The Hardcover And Paperback Editions: 2010035512.

Follow @ReadRiordan
and visit www.DisneyBooks.com